Bind us together Lord
Bind us together
With cords that cannot be broken
Bind us together Lord
Bind us together
Bind us together with love

Bob Gillman
Copyright © Thank You Music 1977

A Call to Christian Harmony

First published 1980

ISBN 0 86065 103 7

All musical arrangements © Kingsway Music 1980
Arranged by John Menlove & Susan van Rooyen
Coordinators: Gerald Coates & John Noble
Musical Director: John Menlove

Printed in Great Britain for
Kingsway Publications Ltd
Lottbridge Drove, Eastbourne, E. Sussex BN23 6NT

Contents

1 Introduction
Overture 7
Bind us together
We are gathering together 14

2 Our relationship with God
The prodigal son (mime/drama) 19
Father I love you 25
Abba, Father 28
I want to learn to appreciate you 30

3 Our relationship with one another
Let us open up ourselves 35
Love me, love my brother 39
Let there be love 42

4 Our relationship with the whole body of Christ
Dry bones (dance/drama) 46
We are being built into a temple 49
It's good to be here 54

5 The Kingdom of God on earth
Finale 58
Thou art worthy to take the book

Notes for Leaders and Musical Directors

By the time you read these notes you will no doubt realise that the musical **Bind Us Together** is intended as a simple aid to promoting Christian harmony. It is offered in the hope and belief that it will provide a framework for local fellowships, churches or groups to express their own desires for unity using the special talents which God has placed within them. It is not intended to be a performance which slavishly adheres to the script, but rather a basis for you to use as much or as little as will serve the Holy Spirit in your particular setting.

There are many points in the programme where you may move into spontaneous worship or prayer, or simply fellowship together. You will find suggestions in the leader's guide booklet. We do want to encourage folk to launch out into new areas of expression of praise and worship, but at the same time it is important not to over-stretch the abilities of your group. Simplicity and confidence are the keynotes. Please do make use of the record or tape; it will help you to sense the spirit of the presentation.

Available separately is a detailed leader's and music director's guide, giving helpful advice on all aspects of a presentation, plus notes on the various mime/drama items which can be added at various points as illustrations to the songs. A musical backing tape is also available. See page 63 for details.

Behind the Bind

'Hello. My name is John Noble. I'm responsible for the team and generally overseeing things. I am so glad that Kingsway asked us in Romford to consider offering **Bind Us Together** to a wider audience and that they suggested that others might like to use it. I'm sure it contains the message for the hour and that God will bless.'

Gerald Coates — 'I'm thrilled to be working with John and the many friends I've known over the years. After a short, successful tour of Scandinavia I was delighted to be approached to promote the British tour and to share the narration.'

'As musical director, I suppose I've carried the main burden of work for this venture — my first major effort since giving myself full time to music. Sue van Rooyen has been an able assistant. My desire is that Christians will be sensitive and free, using all their powers and abilities to worship God together — All the best.' John Menlove

'Ever since I first saw **Bind Us Together** a few years ago, I've been gently encouraging those responsible to make it available to a wider audience! As a member of the Kingsway Music team I'm thrilled that we have been involved in bringing the recording and songbook to fruition.'
Nigel Coltman

'I'm John's wife Christine Noble. I was a Christian for years but underneath was a slightly frustrated actress until I saw that God cares about movement and that drama can be a wonderful way of preaching and prophesying. **Bind Us Together** is a spiritual ambition partly fulfilled for me.'

'You could say that I'm to blame for all this, with God's help of course. 6 years ago at a final Come Together meeting I introduced the song God gave me and was amazed to see it fly around the world.' **Bind Us Together** was written by Bob Gillman in 1974.

Bind us Together

Narration

Introduction: part 1

We are living in thrilling days as all across the globe Christians are becoming aware that God is on the move. Something is happening. There are rumblings and explosions in the Church. People are asking, "What on earth is God doing?" or maybe, "What is God doing on earth?" Well, God is binding us together, right across the world, across the mental and cultural, the physical and denominational barriers that we've built up between us. Right through the difficulties we think stand in his way, right in the midst of what we're doing, God is binding us together.

And it's all well under way. God is speaking and open hearts are hearing and responding. For two decades new light has been dawning through a fresh awareness of the Holy Spirit, and his gifts. In the wake of this joyful experience has come a deep longing for unity and a practical expression of the one body of Christ.

Introduction: part 2

Today the word 'relationships' is ringing out louder than any church bell. We're hearing more and more that Jesus is Lord and that his kingdom is soon to be established for ever on the earth. How far have we come in this awakening? To be honest, not very far, but at least we've left. We've left behind our old life, and we've discovered that the joy of the Lord is our strength. Together we celebrate as creativity is being restored to the people of God. We're singing new songs, we're dancing before him, making a joyful noise to the Lord. In fact God's people positively love to worship him.

So here is **Bind Us Together** — a prophetic cry which has been sung around the world, as many long for a deeper commitment to God and to each other. As darkness spreads bringing with it confusion, loneliness and despair the light of the Church is beginning to shine throughout the earth.

*Overture
with
Bind Us Together

J. Menlove

B. Gillman

Second time only

Narration 1   We live in thrilling days. . . .
Narration 2   Today the word . . .

2nd time to
Bind us Together
Verses 2 and 3

Rall.

10

Verse 3   You are the family of God,
(Music as You are the promise divine,
for verse You are God's chosen desire,
1)   You are the glorious new wine:

Chorus

VERSE 2 Made for the glory of God, _____ Pur-chased by his pre-cious son, Born with a right to be clean, _____ for Je-sus the vic-tory has won: Bind us to-

CHORUS

We Are Gathering Together

♩ = 120 (with pace and strength)

I. Traynar

Lyrics:
We are ga-ther - ing to-ge-ther Un-to the King of kings,

Come in the Spi - rit with joy and peace,

14

Let us make a joy - ful noise ___ un-to the King of kings, _____

Come praise his name,. come on and praise his name. __

name. _____ Let your Spi-rit flow __

from the well _ with-in, _____ Eve-ry-thing that has breath

come and praise_ his name.___ Let us make a

joy - ful noise ___ un-to the King of kings, ___ Come praise his name

___ come on and praise his name._

The prodigal son is essentially related to a mime of the Bible story presented in a modern setting.

It was therefore not considered appropriate to put it on the recording and would only be used in a presentation if sung in association with the mime.

Detailed notes on the mime of **The prodigal son** are included in the leader's guide available separately.

Note
The prodigal son is an optional item in the total presentation, included by the writers to add emphasis to exactly what God has done, to bring us into the relationship he desires with us. The message of **Bind Us Together** will not be diminished, if the song & mime is felt to be beyond the capabilities of any group, and left out.

The Prodigal Son

G. Kiddier

Once up-on a time there was a young boy and 'is dad was a ve-ry rich man. _____ 'e should've been ve-ry 'ap-py _____ be-ing loved as a fa-ther can. _____ But 'e de-ci - ded that 'e want-ed out _____ and 'e took 'is share of the loot. And 'is

Verse 2 (Piano as verse 1)

dad was sad as 'e saw 'is lad walk off in 'is brand new suit, oh yes, 'is

dad was sad as 'e saw 'is lad walk off in 'is brand new suit.

'e walked till 'e came to the big-gest town_ that 'e had ev - er

seen. Straight in - to the rock 'n roll shop where the wo-men and booze_ ain't

free. Look-in' like the last of the big time boys 'e

took the place by storm. 'e was drink - in' the wine and

spend-in' 'is mo-ney, 'e was li - vin' like 'e'd ne-ver been born,___ 'e was

drink-in' the wine_ and spend-in' 'is mo - ney, li - vin' like 'e'd ne-ver been born.

Verse 3

Strange-ly e-nough 'e got ripped off and slung out in - to the street._____ 'e'd 'ad all 'is mo-ney spent for 'im__ and 'e'd no-thing left to eat.._____ So 'e went to the far side of town to find an - oth - er scene, and the peo - ple 'e saw__ with their eyes in the stars, _____

they ne-ver knew 'e'd been. You know the peo-ple 'e saw with their

eyes in the stars, they ne-ver knew 'e'd been.

Verse 4 (Piano as verse 3)

Now the poor boy 'ad no-thing left,____ 'e just a-bout kept 'is 'ead..

____ Think-in' of the mo-ney that 'e had spent and dream-in' of 'is dad and 'is bed_

_____ 'e made up 'is mind that 'e'd go back and 'e'd start_

____ all ov-er a-gain _____ 'e said 'e'd start at the bot-tom and 'e'd

work 'is way up,___ but 'e ne-ver real-ly knew 'is dad, ___ 'e said 'e'd

start at the bot-tom and 'e'd work 'is way up but 'e ne-ver real-ly knew 'is dad.

Bind us Together

Narration

Vertical Ministry

The cross is a great symbol of God's plan for mankind. The vertical is symbolic of our relationship with God; the horizontal of our relationship with each other. But the horizontal cannot exist without the vertical to hold it in place. Therefore our relationship with God must come first. Before we can be bound together we must first be bound to him. Through the Holy Spirit we are called to a renewal of our devotion to Jesus, to fix our eyes on him. In this way we grow to understand what he is really like. The apostle John was devoted to him and so knew him well. In his gospel he wrote, "We beheld his glory, full of grace and truth." The discovery that love and judgement had come together in Jesus set the early Christians free. This was true glory, not sentimental love but real love. Love that dared to discipline, love that put steel into men's lives; surely we want nothing less today.

Prayer

Father, we thank you for your grace which is at work in a new way, restoring our knowledge of your love throughout every denomination, without regard to how we feel it should be done. Amen.

Note
This prayer was spontaneous. You may like to pray your own prayer along these lines.

This might be considered a suitable time to call for a rededication to Jesus.

Father I Love You

D. Bryant

VERSE 1. Fa - ther__ I love you, __ oh,__ do I __ oh how__ I need you, __

2nd time to Coda

My __ oh my   I just can't i-ma-gine __ what life would be like not to have you a-round. __

Fa-ther do I love __ you _____   oh my __ do I __

Verse 2

Fa - ther ___ you thrill ___ me, ___ thrill me through ___ and through ___ I'm so glad ___ to be here _____ with friends who feel the same way too. Fa - ther I'm so hap - py _____ just to sing this song ___ for you. _____ Fa - ther do I love ___ you, ___ you know ___ I do. ___

CODA

D G D A (D bass) G D

D9 G D

Abba, Father

D. Bilbrough

Ab - ba fa - ther let ___ me be yours and yours ___ a - lone, ___ May my will for ev - er be ev - er more your own. ___

Never let my heart grow cold,
nev - er let __ me go. _____ Ab - ba
fa - ther let __ me be yours and yours __ a -

Prayer

lone. _____

I Want To Learn To Appreciate You

John Kennett

Bind us together.

Narration

Horizontal Ministry

On the cross Jesus linked earth with heaven by reconciling us to God —
that's the vertical. He stretched out his hands to reconcile us to one another
— and that's the horizontal. And it is the horizontal that needs a little bit of
attention, to say the least. So far in the church we have emphasised our
individual walk with God. This is vital and necessary, but we have neglected
the fact that we also need each other. We were made to be together. John
says in his letter that if we love God we must love our brother.

Horizontal Ministry   continued

You know, we don't find opening up to one another very easy. It's a big
enough struggle in our own families at times. Misunderstandings can arise,
and then we secretly take offence. We can't even look one another in the eye
for a while, until forgiveness comes. If this is the case with families and
friends, how on earth can we hope to be knit together with people for whom
we've little or no natural love. Not by gritting our teeth. Self-effort and
determination is a certain route to either pride or condemnation. When
Zachariah was building the temple he ran up against similar problems, but
God gave him the key: "Not by might, not by power, but by my Spirit," says
the Lord. If we can just "be still and know God", to quote the psalmist, if we
can let go and let God be God, he will do it for us and through us and in us.
Friendships will blossom, family life will thrive, generosity will flourish as we
respond to the Holy Spirit and learn to love our brothers.

Let Us Open Up Ourselves

♩ = 120 (Relaxed)

Narration 1

Solo voice with choir chorus

P. Bilbrough

We are all a part of one an - o - ther, We can - not hope to live life ful - ly on our own. We each pos - sess a pre - cious part of our Fa - ther's na - ture, And to-

ge-ther we'll be-come that per-fect whole. _____ So let us

CHORUS

op - en up our - selves to one an - o -

ther _____ with-out fear of be - ing hurt or turned a-way,

For we need to con-fess our
weak - ness - es, _ to be cov - ered by our bro-ther's love, _ To be
real and learn our true i - den - ti - ty. _

V. 1 & 3
V. 2 & 4

Instrumental verse behind narration
then to Coda

Verse 2

And God shall sure-ly build his liv-ing tem-ple____ Of peo-ple set com-plete-ly____ free,____ Lov-ing and ap-pre-ci-a-ting one____ an-o-ther,____ En-joy-ing life in its en-ti-re-ty.____ So let us

Repeat Chorus from % to %

Verse 3

Ma-ny shall be drawn to us and won-der____ At the peace and the love and the joy that will ne-ver die.____ They will drink from that stream of liv-ing wa-ter____ Flow-ing out____ from the full-ness of our lives.____ So let us

Repeat Chorus from % to %

Verse 4

So help us to un-der-stand____ each o-ther in a new and liv-ing way,____ Not just ac-cept-ing words that are spo-ken in them-selves.____ But by speak-ing more free-ly____ and lis-ten-ing more clear-ly____ We shall un-der-stand the spi-rit that's with-in.____ So let us

Repeat Chorus from % to %

Narration 2 'You know we don't find opening up. . . .'

CODA   *Rallentando*

Piano

38

Love Me, Love My Brother

B. Gillman

give your-self ___ to his com - mand. ___

%

CHORUS Tails up female harmony
Tails down melody

Love ___ me, love my bro-ther;

That's the way ___ God says it has to be. ___ His

Spi-rit is made flesh in his peo-ple, So

40

you can love the Lord___ now___ in me.   It's

VERSE 2

ea-sy to say ___ we love Fa-ther, ___ For he ain't hard to live___

___ with day by day. ___ But it does-n't mean much to him ___ if we're neg-lect-

-ing ___ To love one an-o-ther come what may. ___

VERSE 3

Have you ev-er felt you want-ed to touch Je-sus, ___ But you

ne-ver feel ___ that you are get-ting through? ___ Well

here's a way ___ that you can meet God sure-ly. ___ Just

Repeat chorus from % to %.

touch that bro-ther sit-ting next to you. ___

CODA   **Slower**

Yes, you can love the Lord now___ in me.

Let There Be Love

D. Bilbrough

na- tion, Cause us O Lord _____ to a- rise. Give us a fresh un-der-

stand-ing of bro-ther-ly love that is real, Let there be love shared a-

mong us, let there be love. _____ (Let there be love.) _____ love.) _____

Last time

1 **2**

43

Our relationship to the whole body of Christ

Bind us together

Narration

Dry Bones

The hand of the Lord was upon me, and carried me out in the Spirit of the Lord, and set me down in the midst of the valley which was full of bones, and caused me to pass by them round about: and, behold, there were very many in the open valley; and, lo, they were very dry.

And he said unto me, son of man, can these bones live? And I answered, O Lord God, thou knowest.

Again he said unto me, Prophesy upon these bones, and say unto them, O ye dry bones, hear the word of the Lord. Thus saith the Lord God unto these bones; Behold, I will cause breath to enter into you, and ye shall live: And I will lay sinews upon you, and will bring up flesh upon you and cover you with skin, and put breath in you, and ye shall live and ye shall know that I am the Lord.

So I prophesied as I was commanded; and as I prophesied, there was a noise, and behold a shaking, and the bones came together, bone to his bone. And when I beheld, lo, the sinews and the flesh came upon them, and the skin covered them above: but there was no breath in them.

Then said he unto me, Prophesy unto the wind, prophesy, son of man, and say to the wind, thus saith the Lord God; come from the four winds, O breath, and breathe upon these slain, that they may live. So I prophesied as he commanded me, and the breath came into them and they lived, and stood up upon their feet, an exceeding great army. Then he said unto me, son of man, these bones are the whole house of Israel: behold, they say, our bones are dried, and our hope is lost: we are cut off for our parts. Therefore prophesy and say unto them, thus saith the Lord: Behold, O my people, I will open your graves, and cause you to come up out of your graves and bring you into the land of Israel, and ye shall know that I am the Lord, when I have opened your graves, O my people, and brought you up out of your graves, and I shall put my Spirit in you and ye shall live, and I shall place you in your own land: then shall ye know that I the Lord have spoken it, and performed it.

Thus saith the Lord.

Authorised Version (King James)
Crown Copyright, extract by permission.

An excellent mime/drama has been worked out by Christine Noble to accompany the above reading. A detailed guide to choreography and stage setting is included in the leader's guide.

Narration

The Church Ministry

Now the bones are being joined together "bone to his bone". Not just a heap of bones getting stuck with each other. No, Christians everywhere are finding out where they belong and God is joining the bones together. Sometimes we don't fit too well at first because it's not always easy to see things from God's point of view. There's a rattling as we find our place. In fact many people are allowing disillusionment to hinder them just at the time when God would complete the work. But if we are faithful it will happen. Indeed already flesh is coming upon the bones that are fused together; the life of God is being breathed into a living body. A new corporate man with Christ the head. It's an organism not an organisation, it is dependent on life, not on rules and regulations, and that life is the life of God.

(Quiet piano start here)
The first Christians sought God together. They devoted themselves to fellowship, to common meals, to the apostles' doctrine and to prayer. Together they were filled with God's Spirit. This corporate experience of the Holy Spirit will bring us to a deeper understanding, appreciation and love for each other. So God will bring his body to maturity and to boldness, and as a mighty army clad in the whole armour of God we will come against Satan and we shall win. The enemies of God will be crushed not only beneath the feet of Jesus but, because the church is his body, under our feet as well. We are triumphant in Jesus by his grace.

Prayer

Father, we respond to your desire that we be built together, and we give you our whole-hearted consent to shape our lives. There is, Lord, no place we would rather be than in your house.

Note
Again this prayer may give you food for thought. Here is a good moment to respond to what God is saying.

A simple mime is recommended to accompany the song **We are Being Built Into A Temple.** A number of people with the letters of the word Temple attached to them, work out together the fact that they are letters, and co-operate in lining up to form the complete word. Full details of the mime can be found in the leader's guide.

We Are Being Built Into A Temple

I. Traynar

We are be-ing— built— in-to a tem-ple— fit for God's own dwell-ing place,— In-to the house of God — which is the church The pill-ar and — the ground of

As pre-cious stones_ that Je-sus owns

Fash-ioned by_ his wond-rous grace.

And as we love_

_ and trust each oth-er_____

So the build-ing grows and grows.

We are be-ing built in-to a tem-ple

Fit for God's own dwell-ing place,

In-to the house of God which is the church,

The pi-llar and the ground of truth, As pre-cious stones that Je-sus owns fash-ioned by his wond-rous grace And as we love

Prayer

It's Good To Be Here

D. Bilbrough and N. Butterworth

SOLO Verse 1

It's good to be here, __ My friends are near, __

It's good to know __ they love you too.

Just think-ing of you __ I don't have a clue __

Why you love us like__ you do.__ Hal - le - lu -

Hal - le - lu__   Hal - le - lu__

FEMALE
VOICES

__ jah!   Hal - le - lu - jah!_____

Verse 2

(Descant)

(Melody) I just don't de - serve__   to be here   at all,__

it seems so strange__ to__ me__ and yet__

The light of the world__   has shined in   on me.__

My eyes are wet,   don't__ be _ sur - prised.__   I'm so

so grate-ful, ___ so grate-ful, ___

grate-ful, _____ I'm so grate-ful. ___

Verse 3

Gone with the past ___ Of things that don't last. ___

To know ___ you is life ___ for ___ ev - er - more.

As things all a - round ___ Are fall-ing to the ground, My heart is soar-ing like ___ a

CODA

lark. Hal-le-lu - jah! Hal-le-lu -

Hal-le-lu - jah! Hal-le-lu - jah!

Repeat 8 times or ad lib

The kingdom of God on earth

Bind us together

Narration

The Kingdom

To many, the body as an army is a new concept, but it's armies and battles from which kingdoms are built. Jesus taught his disciples to pray, "Father, your kingdom come, your will be done on earth as it is in heaven." Heaven is being established here on earth, the new Jerusalem is coming down from heaven to earth. The promise is, "The meek shall inherit the earth." Right here is where God is going to establish his kingdom and accomplish his objectives. Jesus is coming back, back to earth; he's coming back, back to a beautiful bride, ready and waiting eagerly for his return. He's coming back, back to a transparent city prepared for a rule of peace and love and justice.

It will happen if we start at the beginning with Jesus, if we will go on with Jesus, if we will remain faithful to the end with Jesus, because he is the Alpha and the Omega, the beginning and the end. All glory be to him for ever. Amen.

Revelation 21:1-7

Then I saw a new heaven and a new earth; for the first heaven and the first earth had passed away, and the sea was no more. And I saw the holy city, new Jerusalem, coming down out of heaven from God, prepared as a bride adorned for her husband; and I heard a great voice from the throne saying, "Behold, the dwelling of God is with men. He will dwell with them and they shall be his people, and God himself will be with them; he will wipe away every tear from their eyes, and death shall be no more, neither shall there be mourning nor crying nor pain any more, for the former things have passed away."

And he who sat upon the throne said. "Behold, I make all things new." Also he said, "Write this, for these words are trustworthy and true." And he said to me, "It is done! I am the Alpha and the Omega, the beginning and the end. To the thirsty I will give water without price from the fountain of the water of life: he who conquers shall have this heritage, and I will be his God and he shall be my son.

Thou Art Worthy To Open The Book

This is the climax of the presentation and will achieve this with the dynamic of the music and lyrics.

You may feel the spiritual atmosphere will be enhanced by a mime included in the leader's guide, which portrays the adoration and praise we should give to the One who is worthy — Jesus.

Recommended chord sequence for instruments and angelic voices behind Revelation 21 reading.

Narration

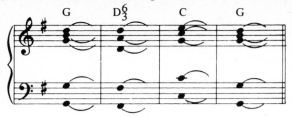

Key change into 'Thou art worthy'

Thou Art Worthy To Take The Book

T. Pullen & I. McDonald

ran - som men for God.___ From eve - ry tribe and tongue___ and

peo - ple and na - tion and hast made them a king - dom and

priests_ to our God and they___ shall reign, shall___

reign_ on _ earth.

Thou art wor-thy to take the book_ And to o-pen its seals,_ For

thou wast slain _ and_ by thy blood.didst_ ran - som men for God.

From eve-ry tribe_ and tongue_____ and_ peo - ple and na - tion and hast made_them a king - dom and priests_to our God   and they____ shall reign, shall____ reign___ on ___ earth.

Aids to Christian Harmony

LP
Cassette
Songbook
Leader & Music Directors Guide
Backing Tape

Above are aids available to folk wishing to present **Bind Us Together.**
The Leader and Music Director's Guide contains valuable information
covering all aspects of presentation including details and prices of materials,
putting together a choir and musicians, copyright guidance, narration and
leading in worship. Full details of the mime, drama, and dance items are
also included. The cost is £1, post free (in the UK) from:

Kingsway Music

Lottbridge Drove, Eastbourne, E Sussex, Great Britain BN23 6NT

Kingsway Music present

SONGS OF FELLOWSHIP

As in the days of the psalmist when fresh experiences of the dealings of God led to new songs — so today new songs are being written as God continues to make Himself real to His people.

Dove 47   DVCS 147
A New Song
Songs of Fellowship Vol. 1

Sing unto the Lord a new song/We have come into this Place/Jesus is changing me/Our God reigns/Arise Shine/We are being built into a temple/Abba Father/Jesus stand among us/Bind us Together/Building a people of power & 6 others.

Dove 53   DVCS 153
City of God
Songs of Fellowship Vol. 2

City O City/My life is really blest/Jesus take me as I am/Come & Praise Him, Royal Priesthood/We shall be as one/Thank you Jesus/ Take my yoke/I will sing unto the Lord & 8 others.

KMR 316   KMC 316
Our eyes have seen the King
Songs of Fellowship Vol. 3

Victory/Our eyes have seen the King/The Lord has built up Zion/O Lord you've done great things/We'll sing a new song/The kingdom of this world/Behold a new day/Ascribe to the Lord/Lord God heavenly King/The Lord reigns/I will extol you/Let us come and worship.

KMR 328   KMC 328
Draw near to God
Songs of Fellowship Vol. 4

Jesus, Jesus, Jesus/You shall go out with joy/We are a Kingdom/For we see Jesus/Sing to our God/I will rejoice/Promised land/Jesus name above all names/Rustling/Worthy art thou/My heart overflows/Jesus come closer now to me/I stand before the presence/I receive your love/Draw near to God.

KMR 329   KMC 329
Emmanuel
Songs of Fellowship Vol. 5

Great & Marvellous/O give thanks/Halleluia, my father/Lion of Judah/I delight to do thy will/Lord we want to thank you/My Lord, He is the fairest/River wash over me/Thank you Jesus/Where you go I will go/Emmanuel/& 4 others.

Songs of Fellowship songbook
containing 53 recent praise & worship compositions including: Come & Praise Him/Jesus stand among us/Bind us Together/Jesus how lovely you are/Jesus take me as I am/Sing unto the Lord/Abba Father/For I'm building a people.

Available from Christian record stockists
Published by

Kingsway Music

Lottbridge Drove
Eastbourne
East Sussex BN23 6NT